Also by G.D. Harding

advice from my dog

—

Girl,
It has been a
Pleasure to share
the diamond with
you.

Garlso [illegible]

advice from my dog

Tales from Nantucket & the World

G.D. HARDING

NICKEL DRAFT PUBLISHING
NANTUCKET

ADVICE FROM MY DOG
Nickel Draft Publishing / August 2003

The text of this book was set in 10 pt Book Antiqua.

Published in the United States by Nickel Draft Publishing, Nantucket

ISBN: 0-9744411-0-4

Printed in the United States of America

first edition

For Bumpa

The luckiest man I ever met

contents

acknowledgments

For Inspiration & Ideas

Nicko Abraham, Jon Allen, Todd Billings, Anne Boginski, Derek Boston, Jon Brennan, Kyle Brown, Tom Davidson, Josh Davis, Joe Gallagher, Laura Gallagher, Dewey Golub, Hal Gould, Jeff Herman, Mary Jennings, Steffen Kondi, Mark Larsen, Tyler Lauback, Tom Lightbody, Terry Londen, Chris Mackie, Jon McGarr , Paul Murphy, Mike Palm, Brian Reeder, Jason Ross, Carol Smith, Brian Sullivan, Donald Sullivan, Mike Sullivan, Firtz VonRuhmor, Robert Walker, Brian Williams, Dan Woods, Zeuss, & Stephanie Sproule who thought she wouldn't make it in.

For Edits & Advice

Mike Sullivan, Brian Sullivan, Stephanie Sproule, Jay Hanley, & Paul Murphy

For Everything

Mom, Dad, Will, Nana, Magic & Luke Gutelius

PROLOGUE

prologue

For Christmas my brother gave me "The Book of Embraces" by Eduardo Galeano. The book is a collection of short stories, many of which had me laughing out loud Christmas morning. None of the stories are longer then 2 pages which is great for me being of the generation that invented a.d.d.

When I returned to Nantucket I thought a lot about that book and all the funny stories I had heard over the years from friends, family, and the strange man at the end of the bar. Then I sat down, looked out over the frozen harbor, and wrote one down. Nantucket seems to have a way of bringing out the creativity in everyone, especially in the winter when if you don't have some kind of hobby you go even more insane then you allready are.

Six months later the snow began to melt and I had a hundred stories. The following pages contain seventy five of those. I hope you enjoy reading them as much as I enjoyed hearing them, living them, or hallucinating them as the case may be.

Everyone has a book in them, here's mine.

G.D. Harding

Nantucket, August 2003

FROZEN MUDSLIDE

perfect for a summer's day

shark

Frank was a man who would never admit that he was getting older. Every year spent sitting on a barstool he added an inch to his waistline. Instead of buying bigger pants Frank just kept wearing them lower. "Still got a 32 inch waist," he would brag, his belt invisible under his beer gut.

Frank caught a 5 foot shark with his friends one weekend when the bar was being redone. Instead of throwing it back or bringing it home to horrify his wife, Frank took it down to the end of the fishing pier. He jumped off the end with the shark in his arms and tied it to one of the supports a few feet under water.

The next day was perfect and the beach nearby was packed with sunbathers. Frank went for a swim out towards the end of the pier, when he got out over his head he dove down and shot his body high out of the water yelling as long as he could before he submerged, "Shaaaaark." On the way back down Frank continued towards the support at the bottom of the pier and untied the shark.

As mothers ran into the water to grab their children and body surfers fled the waves with Olympic speed, Frank wrestled with the shark. Families regrouped in the dunes well away from the dangers of the ocean, Frank continued to wrestle with the shark thrashing around in the water. Teenagers stood speechless dripping on the hot sand, Frank wrestled on. Father's and sons watched together trying to see who had the upper hand; Frank disappeared for a while, but wouldn't give up.

Finally, a full fifteen minutes after he had warned the beach of the danger Frank emerged from the sea. He walked slowly out of the surf, exhausted from the battle, stopped a few feet from the damp sand and looked around at all the people watching him. Frank stood in silence, the beast slung over his right shoulder. He then dropped the shark on the sand and walked through the crowd and on towards his barstool in town.

'Man saves beach" the headline read the next day, "kills shark with bare hands."

geography

One summer Jeff went out for a long kayak trip around the harbor. Kayaking gives him a chance to hear all the sounds that are normally covered up by the noise of the world around him. Once the sun submerged into the ocean and the crickets made their presence felt he headed in.

Jeff pulled his kayak on shore and a tourist walked over to him. "Hi there. I watched you come all the way in, you sure were a long way out there." The sounds of the ocean were once again covered by the man's voice.

Jeff looked up from his vessel and smiled at the man as he caught his breath, "Once a year I make the trip over to the island from Hyannis," he said.

"Wow, that's quite a trip," said the man, startled trying to comprehend the journey, "how long does it take you?"

"Well, I like to take my time" Jeff began, "Hyannis to Edgartown, about four hours, but it seemed to take a lot longer tonight."

"Edgartown?" said the tourist raising his voice as he pronounced the end of the word. "Isn't Edgartown on Martha's Vineyard?"

"Ya," said Jeff, "just south of Oak Bluffs. I usually walk, but I'm a little tired tonight, so I think I'll catch a cab."

"But ...this is Nantucket," said the man certain of his geography, "Martha's Vineyard is a different island, twenty miles from here."

Jeff stood silently looking at the man and then swore under his breath. He pulled his kayak off the sand, stepped back into the cool water, and paddled out towards the open ocean. The tourist stood in silence as he watched Jeff disappear towards the dark spot where the sun had set.

Once again Jeff heard the sounds of the water splashing against the side of the boat, the crickets rubbing their legs, and the soft hum of the world around him. Silly tourist, he thought to himself as he paddled towards the beach.

pizza boy

Chris drives the harbor launch, and therefore has the pleasure of ferrying a lot of people with more money then they know what to do with to and from their boats.

A couple of years ago such a man was asked to be on his way after he had a party on his yacht where he dresses up as a priest. They probably would have let that slide, but all the strippers on board dressed as nuns was a little too much for the quaint harbor to take.

The yachtsman was also a collector of military memorabilia and somehow had purchased a working antique tank. Unfortunately other then training for an invasion he didn't have a lot of opportunity to drive it.

One of the rites of passage being a teenager is to harass the local pizza delivery guy. Whether it's ordering a pie for the house next door and stealing the unguarded pizzas out of his car, or answering the door in a cow costume, it's something you have to do growing up. When you're a multi millionaire you can really bring the fun to a whole new level.

The yachtsman sat in the tank in its garage one day while his friend ordered a couple of large pizza's from the house. When the pizza boy came to the front door the friend opened up and was handed the pies in exchange for a twenty dollar bill. As the boy turned to go back to his car the two watched as the yachtsman drove over the boy's Ford Escort in the tank and continued on into the back yard.

The boy stared in silence at the flattened pizza flag on the flattened car. "Sorry about that," said the man at the door, "he must not have seen you parked there." He handed the boy a check for fifteen thousand dollars and went back into the house.

statistics

I went down to Fat Lady's beach on Nantucket one summer day to meet my friend Terry. Terry was lounging with some people enjoying the day and a few pony Bud's. The pony beers are the half size bottles that they gave you on the shuttle from Boston to New york, when you didn't have time for a full 12 ounces.

Later I came to realize that the pony beers are perfect for the beach, because you drink them before they get warm. On this particular day I was not as wise as I am today.

"Terry," I asked "what are you drinking the mini Buds for?" Terry polished one off, and looked it over in his hand, "Padding the stats."

bass

Sully is a real estate salesman. Part of selling a house on Nantucket, he tells me, is selling the island. After the client sees the sunset over the Atlantic, hears the quiet of the waves breaking on the miles of coast, or feels a fish hit and run off into the deep waters, the small square footage of the master bathroom is a much easier sell.

Once such client was an avid fisherman and Sully had mentioned to him that September was a great time to catch striped bass, or stripers as they are often referred to. The client and his wife made plans to come out and Sully emailed them about how on Saturday he would take Dan out and they would get some stripers.

Sully is a pretty good real estate salesman, but not an exceptional speller. Later that day he got an angry phone call back from Dan's wife. "Sully, I understand that you want Dan to have a good time and I'm all for that. However, I think inviting Dan out to look at naked women is inappropriate. It is our vacation and I do not want you and my husband going out and getting strippers.

chauffeur

Tom loved two things, old cars and his dog Zeus. He came into possession of a vintage right hand drive Mercedes that had been shipped over from England.

"It's a work of art," he told me when I asked about his newest acquisition, "she's a pearl 1969 190 SL roadster, with screaming red leather."

Zeus lumbered up and down on the beach behind us. The dog was a 160 lb black Newfoundland with the biggest head I've ever seen. Zeus was very friendly, the problem was if Zeus liked you too much and decided to get on top of you and lick your face you weren't going anywhere until he was ready.

"How do you like the steering wheel being on the wrong side," I asked.

Tom laughed out loud. "I don't mind it."

A few days' later I met my friend Heather in town. "You'll never believe it," she said, obviously excited, "I just saw this huge black dog fly through town driving a Mercedes.

the other side

Kyle's gaze drifted between the beautiful boats floating in Bar Harbor, and the beautiful blondes floating in the bar. Jon simultaneously poured one of the girls a frozen drink while he lit another's cigarette. "...and that's how you know that the US is secretly being run from Canada," he explained. The women laughed hysterically. Their heads slowly turned in unison, as if connected, when Jon walked to the other end of the bar.

"Where's the rest of the crew today Kyle?" He asked.

"Jon, this drink is unbelievable," yelled one of the blondes' from across the bar.

"I know, can you believe it?" Jon responded with his back turned. The girls again burst into hysterics.

"I should be taking notes," said Kyle sneaking a glance at the girls past his friend."

"It's not me Kyle," Jon answered. He watched a group of guys standing in a circle far enough from the women to avoid an uncomfortable silence between the two groups, but close enough so they wouldn't miss a glimpse of their tongues licking the foam from their lips. Jon rested his elbows comfortably on the varnished wood and wedged a lime into the clear bottle. "On the other side, I'm just like you."

blue laws

During a brief hiatus between colleges a group of us traveled to Nantucket for the fourth of July. On Sunday Tyler and I woke up early and walked into town for lunch.

We both ordered a seafood salad sandwich and a beer. "I'm sorry," said the waitress, "but the state says we can't serve beer until after twelve on Sundays."

Tyler and I looked at each other surprised at the bad news. I ordered a water, Tyler sat in thought looking at the menu and then back at the waitress, "What about hard alcohol?" he asked.

fudge

Cheryl Fudge runs a clothing shop by the same name.

"If I had a dollar for every fat guy who came in, took one look around, and left I'd be a rich man," an employee once told me.

gold rush

Being a temp worker is a fascinating existence. While between colleges I worked as a security guard at a race track, answered phones for gamblers anonymous, a video game tester, a deranged janitor in a haunted house, a mall store builder, and a Christmas tree shipper.

On every job there is always the legend of the temp worker who got hired to work for the company full time. The tale is usually told by the elder temp at that company who has been working as a temp in the same place for 3 years.

Everybody hates the temp. Nobody cares if the temp quits, because tomorrow there's a new temp. The temp is a nameless worker as interchangeable as the bottle atop the water cooler where the other employees joke about them. The temp never works for the company he is at, but always through the temp agency. Therefore, if the temp gets hurt, the temp agency has to pay the bills. Send the temp to check if there's a gas leak.

The converse is that the temp is never around to answer why none of the flowers came up in the spring. The temp has moved on to his next adventure, screwing up a completely different job.

One day I spent 6 hours digging a trench in the Arizona sun. An old timer worked along side us and told us stories of his life. People always save the best stories for times when no normal people are around.

We talked and dug, and took breaks. Taking breaks is very important to a temp worker. The hole got deeper and the day got longer until some-one plunged their shovel into the dirt and there was a sudden fizzing sound. The ground beneath our feet became moist. We climbed out and watched the days work fill in with muddy water.

Our boss for the day walked over. He shook his head as he looked at the mud filled hole. "You guys are going to have to shovel all the mud out. Jump on back in there; we've already lost a half day out of you."

I looked down at our hole. My clothes will be ruined, my feet will be soaked, and I'll be caked in mud for the whole ride home.

The elder statesman was surveying the scene, he didn't seem as dis-traught as the rest of the crew. He looked over at the kid who had hit the water line. "You just struck gold boy," he said with a smile, "that's it for me."

that guy

While a freshman in college I was in the laundry room folding my clothes when I came across an undergarment that I had never seen before. I held up the thong to examine it further when I felt someone watching me. I looked up, a slightly older student stood in the hallway staring blankly at me. We shared an awkward silence where I can only imagine he pictured me in the thong, and then he nodded and went on his way.

The next semester a girl I was trying to impress knocked a beer over in my lap. If I leave now I'll blow my chance with the brunette, but nobody is going to want to hang out with the guy with the wet crotch. I went to the men's room in search of towels but found only a hand dryer. First scanning the restroom I lifted my leg up on top of the sink and pressed my crotch as close to the dryer as I could. My eyes were fixed on the bathroom door so as soon as someone entered I could pull my leg down and pretend to dry my hands.

Eventually my pants began to dry, the whirr of the dryer suddenly stopped, and there was a brief silence. Not a normal silence, but a silence that is too quiet, a silence without background noise. I turned my head away from the door, and looked back over my shoulder. I hadn't seen him since the laundry room; this did answer the question of whether he still was in school. He nodded his remembrance and walked out the door.

April 31st is exactly half a year away from Halloween and some girls got the idea to throw a half-Halloween party. I came into the possession of full length bunny costume, slid it on, grabbed a twelve pack of the cheapest beer in Arizona, and went to the fiesta. The school year was coming to an end, we partied like it was all ready over.

I woke up the next morning in a room filled with stuffed animals and a list of questions that I didn't want to think about until I was home. I slid out of bed and quietly put on the bunny costume, grabbed my head, and snuck out of the house. Once outside I got my bearings and took the back roads towards the dorms. As those of you who have walked home in a bunny suit in Phoenix in spring can attest, it's hot. The only thing I had going for me was it was early in the morning and by the halfway point no cars had driven by.

Then I heard the crescendo of tires on pavement and gave a wave as a pickup drove by. Nobody isn't going to notice a guy in a bunny suite walking down the street in April, so why not just wave. The break lights came on an arm motioned for me to get in. I had never seen this car, but long before I reached the passenger door and got in I knew who would be driving.

grass

While in college I worked as a landscaper. I liked to cut grass and let my mind wander in whatever direction the breeze blew it. Back and forth, and back and forth, painting long green stripes across the ground.

One spring we planted a new lawn for a customer. As we drove by in the truck one summer's day I noticed that it hadn't grown in as well as we had hoped. I asked Brian why this was. "Well," he began, "they might not of watered it enough, or it might have gotten burned out from too much sun, could've been aggressive jiggers, or they could've over watered it... whatever it was, it definitely wasn't our fault."

BEER

simple, cool

phone number

I listened to the pretty voice on the answering machine, waited for the beep, and hung up the phone.

What do you do when you call someone for the first time and they're not home? Is it best to leave a message? What if they don't call back, do you call them again, how long do you wait? Then do you leave another message or do you not leave a message and keep calling back until someone answers?

"I never give out my number, it's too confusing, and half the time guys never call," Stephanie told me when I enquired about a female view on the subject. "I just give out my address now, that way if they really want to go out they can just stop by and we go."

acky

One Sunday Nicko came to his parent's house after watching the Patriots game. When he stepped out of his truck, Acky, his mother's white Springer spaniel bounced around happily thrilled at his arrival. After a few tosses of Acky's favorite stick Nicko relieved himself on a nearby snow-bank, and then went inside.

Nicko chatted with his mother about the weather and the great goal-line stand. When he was ready to leave and his mother opened the door for him Nicko pointed in amazement at a yellow A-C-K-Y signed in the snow. "Mom," he screamed, "look what the dog did."

turkey

In Massachusetts Thanksgiving morning high school football teams around the state play their arch rival. It's the biggest game of the season. All the alumni are home, the stands are full, and bragging rights for the year are at stake.

When my father was in high school he was quarterback for a team that was a little south of greatness. They knew, however, that if they could win against Wayland on Thanksgiving that is all that would be remembered. To accomplish this feat the "what's a matta" play was devised.

My father and the Wildcats didn't dissapoint the hometown crowd and found themselves down by just five points with the clock winding down. As they looked up from their own 35 they knew it was time. The Wildcats lined up and locked in position. All except the tight end, who turned around and waved towards my father "hey, hey wait a second." My father stood behind center and looked at the end, a blank expression on his face. "What's a matta?" he asked. No sooner had he uttered "matta" then the ball was snapped and the line surged forward. While the warriors stood watching the confused end the quarterback scrambled 65 yards for the touchdown.

The Wildcats had won. For the first time in years, the Wildcats had won. While mothers went home to prepare the day's feast, and fathers to retell with pride their account of the great upset, the Wildcats went to celebrate.

The victory celebration had to be sandwiched in between the game and Thanksgiving dinner, so for the players the celebration had to be condensed in hours, but not necessarily in consumption. By the time the dinner bell rang the crew was pretty well cocked. However, everyone looked sober as a judge compared to young Carol.

The toughest play call for the Wildcat football team was still left to be made. Who was going to help the post game MVP into her house for Thanksgiving dinner? In the end the quarterback was elected as the most suitable ambassador, and so my father found himself with Carol's arm around his shoulders walking her into the house.

An extended family was seated around the table waiting for the daughter of the house to come home. My father accepted the tables' congratulations on the victory, trying not to seem impolite, and yet praying with all his might to get out of there before Carol opened her mouth and let the family know that she was not merely drunk but ...drunk.

For a moment he thought he might succeed, the questions wound down and Carol leaned against the wall quietly staring at the Turkey in all its Thanksgiving glory. Then she spoke, "Mom," Carol began "What did you do to the dog?"

christmas tree

The Murphy's Christmas tree was the pride of the family. One year Murph's parents went away a couple of weeks before Christmas. Murph and his brother Matt were given $300 and left with a single task; get the best Christmas tree in Duxbury.

As the door shut and Mr. & Mrs. Murphy left for the airport Murph and Matt begin preparations for the week's festivities. Friends were called, kegs were bought, and before too long Murph and his brother found themselves sitting on the couch, their parents return hours away and no Christmas tree.

The brothers scraped through the remaining funds, $13.85. You can't get a Christmas tree in Duxbury, or Deluxe-bury, as it is often called, for $13.85.

As was often the case, Matt had a plan. The brothers Murphy drove a few miles away, parked the car, and walked into the woods. "There will be plenty of Christmas trees here," Matt promised. As the brothers looked around the woods Matt's plan began to lose steam, not even Charlie Brown would have been satisfied with a tree from this forest.

The brothers forged on looking high and low for a suitable centerpiece for the family's Christmas. Then Murph spotted them, a row of pine trees escalating in height like a giant triangle. Trees groomed to perfection, trees watered when the sun got hot, tree whose branches were shaken when the snow fell too heavy, trees which lined the fairway of the Duxbury golf club's 18th hole.

"This is the nicest tree we've ever had," Mr. Murphy said, beaming with pride as he came into the house. "It must be ten feet tall, and the shape is perfect. If I didn't know any better I'd think you boys hijacked this tree from Rockefeller Center."

Mr. and Mrs. Murphy dropped their bags and the family retired to the living room to admire the great tree. No sooner had they put their feet up then there was a knock at the door.

"Afternoon Officer Fordy."

"Happy Holidays Mr. Murphy, I'm sorry to bother you. A pine tree has been stolen from the Duxbury golf course and several witnesses say they saw your boys walking down the street in the area carrying a tree. That's quite a tree you have there in your living room."

"Yes it is Officer Fordy, my boys and I just got it this morning at Trapello's Hardware."

"Okay Mr. Murphy, you have a merry Christmas, and tell the boys to be good."

As the door slammed shut and the boy's father turned to look at them, the two knew right away that there would be a few less presents under the giant Christmas tree.

southpaw

My second tour of duty at college was at a school with a large Thai population. Having grown up in a sheltered community it was nice to see a different point of view, especially concerning global issues. One of my Thai friends remarked to me one afternoon, "I never knew there was so many problems in America until I watch the Jerry Springer show."

Years later Jon appeared on a similar show. Jon is a pretty normal guy by talk show standards, and got duped into appearing on one of those "I have something to tell you shows." Apparently he hadn't seen a lot of talk shows and was under the impression that sometimes good things happen.

Jon's girlfriend brought him on national TV to let him know she was seeing someone else. There was the inevitable skirmish with the new boyfriend and Jon was transformed by the magic of television into a "where do they find these people" guy.

After the show aired Jon had to make the rounds to perform damage control with pretty much everyone he had ever met. I asked him if he were to go back in time what he would do differently. Jon looked quizzically skyward for quite a while. "You are never really prepared, no matter how much you think you are prepared for anything. I made the same mistake everyone makes, I got so caught up in the emotion of everything that I couldn't think rationally.

What I should have done is gone in southpaw. You only get one shot and everyone is looking for the big right hand. If I went in like I was a lefty faking a big left hook I think I could have floored him with a straight right. I've got a great right. If I were to go back in time I would go in southpaw, like in Rocky II.

spice of life

"Five incredible Hulk shots," a man yelled at the bartender.

Mike spilled a couple different types of liquor into the shaker with some ice and poured the man his drinks. When there was a lull in the chaos he walked over to the end of the bar. "I must have made fifty different types of shots tonight; one eyed chinchilla, Alaskan chainsaw, and we had a huge run on flaming midgets."

"What's an incredible Hulk shot?" I asked.

"Gin, fruit juice, and triple sec," he answered.

"That's an incredible Hulk," I questioned, "it's not even green."

Mike looked over his shoulder with a grin as he went to handle a new rush of tourists, "That's all of them."

coffee

While in college my brother told me one morning he woke up on the couch at a coffee shop and had no idea how he got there.

"When you woke up did you get a cup of coffee?" I asked.

He shook his head, "I just left," he told me.

mr. wiggles

Connecticut is a pretty state with a lot of open farmland and a fair number of gentlemen's clubs. Most of the farmland is really just open fields and not really inhabited by farmers, and most of the gentlemen's clubs are not really inhabited by gentlemen, but it is a nice state none the less.

Todd and his friends were driving towards a favorite strip joint one evening when they passed a field with a bunch of goats. Todd pulled over and after a bit of negotiating they were able to purchase one of the herd. The goat was loaded into the back of the truck and the boys continued on their way.

When they got to the strip joint the boys led the goat toward the front door. Being a bouncer at a strip joint you see your share of oddities, but this was too much for the large man to take. "You can't bring that thing in here," the bouncer insisted. The boys were not about to leave their new friend in the truck to miss all the fun, so a bit of an argument ensued. "The goat's got the ten bucks cover," the boys argued, "This is discrimination."

As the argument began to escalate a middle aged man walked over and put his hand on Todd's shoulder. "This place sucks. What kind of strip joint won't let you bring your goat in," the man said. "Follow me boys we'll go to my place."

Todd, his friends, and the goat followed the man down the street to his club. They walked in, stuck a hundred dollar bill on the goat's horn, and led him up to the stage. That was one night Mr. Wiggles will never forget.

jury duty

My father came home early from the court house. He had been selected for jury duty seven times and always got out of it. "It's very simple," he told me, "when the prosecutor comes in the room you never take your eyes off him."

"Do you say anything?" I asked.

"No, never say anything. You just stare blankly at him, it really freaks them out and they always just dismiss you without saying why," my father explained, "and don't blink."

scarecrow

When "trick or treating" there is no greater sight then a bowl of candy left unattended. There's usually a sign next to the bowl which instructs you to take only one or two pieces, but as a kid you read "first come first serve."

When kids would come to Jay's porch they would be treated to such a vision, a giant tub sitting in the arms of a scarecrow. On the scarecrow's chest was a sign that read "Please take only two pieces, the scarecrow is watching."

The kids would tromp onto the porch and most of them headed the warning and took just a few pieces. Eventually a young boy would arrive who lifted the bowl to his pillow case to dump the full bounty into his sack.

"The kids sure are getting fast these days," Jay's father told me one Halloween.

"What do you mean?" I asked "And where did you get that scarecrow costume?"

signs

For years Mike worked as a printer. As he cleaned the press he would sometimes recall a time in 1947 when he "had a cup of coffee" with the Red Sox.

Mike played minor league baseball right out of high school. Finally, one spring day he got the call. He was a kid living his dream, sitting in the bullpen at Fenway Park. Mike was called into the game in the sixth inning and jogged to the mound. Thirty thousand eyes watched as he palmed the rosin bag and looked in toward the catcher for the sign.

The catcher was a veteran Boston player named Birdie Tebbits. Birdie fingered a combination of one's and two's to Mike, but the pitcher shook his head. After another sign by the catcher Mike got the one he was looking for and fired the ball towards home plate. The ball was returned past him much harder. The rest of the afternoon was much the same for Mike; he would shake Birdie off, throw his pitch, and turn and watch as it sailed past.

After the game as he sat with his arm wrapped in ice some reporters came by his locker. "Mike," one of the reporters asked, "your a young kid pitching your first game in the pro's, you've never seen any of the hitters before and have no idea what type of pitches they like. Birdie Tebbits behind the plate has been playing pro ball for over ten years. Why did you shake off so many of his signs today?" Mike smiled and said, "I can't throw the shit he was asking for."

bowling

Derek walked into the local bowling alley, took off his Nike's and walked over to the counter. "Ten and a half," he told the man.

The attendant picked out a pair of shoes in his size and placed them on the counter. "How many frames would you like?" he asked.

Derek looked back at the man and opened his mouth, "I don't want to bowl," he said, "I just want to rent the shoes."

the straw

Steve admired the sports car slowly rotating on the expo floor. The palomino leather seats reflected off a British racing green finish. Under the hood lived a shiny V8 with sequential fuel injection and electronic throttle control giving 350 Horsepower at 5200 rpm and 405 horsepower at 6000 rpm, all mated to a high performance six-speed manual transmission.

Accompanying the machine in its eternal spin was a tall beauty with tanned legs, dark hair, and eyes that matched the glossy finish. On paper she was as perfect as the car she leaned against, but there was something missing, something that you couldn't quite pick out that kept her working at car shows instead of in the pages of a magazine.

Steve's eyes traversed the sleek lines of metal from the front tire to the hood, to the door, then straight back to the tail-lights where they followed the long legs to her stomach, her chest and into her eyes. "Soo," he began, "does..." But he didn't get a chance to finish.

The model cut him off, "Do I come with the car?" She asked mockingly, "do you know how many times I hear that god dammed line every day? I am so sick of you scum bags coming here and eyeing me up and down with your pick up lines and your fake Italian suits."

Steve stood silently for a moment and then remembered that he wasn't talking anymore and shut his mouth. He turned quietly and walked back to his friends. They stopped their conversation. Four sets of eyes looked at Steve waiting for him to speak when one of his friends broke the silence, "Soo," Steve's friend asked, "am I right? Does traction control come standard?"

shopping spree

When Mike was in college he got the idea that Mudd, a broke friend of his, should win a sixty second shopping spree at the supermarket. Somehow he talked a student with a credit card into sponsoring the event and preparations were made.

Mudd was given lots of advice from everyone on the best strategy to make the most of his prize. Some said he should go straight for the steaks, others advised that he fill up the cart with pasta so his winnings would last him the remaining 5 years of his college career. In the end Mudd decided he would figure it all out once the whistle sounded, like he always did.

That Sunday Mudd, Sully, the kid with the credit card, and a large number of Mudd's supporters went down to the local Supermarket for the event. As women leisurely browsed the baking needs aisle and chatted about the concert on the town green this coming Wednesday, Mudd gripped the bar of the shopping cart and rocked back and forth behind the duct tape starting line. Cashiers stopped what they were doing for a moment and stared at the large group of people standing around Mudd and his cart. Before they had a chance to ask what was going on the kid with the credit card raised his hand in the air.

After a brief moment of silence, his hand dropped and the sound of the whistle, borrowed from the phys-ed. department, pierced the air. Mudd took off down the first aisle and the crowd erupted in cheers, the kid with the credit card shouted out the time in five second intervals. The store manager ran toward the mob to find out what could possibly be going on at 10:30 on Sunday morning.

When all was tallied, Mudd had stuffed $234.15 worth of groceries into his cart and one new squirt gun. The food only lasted a few weeks, the Green Castle, Indiana Triple A however, was never the same.

second to last

In high school, the football coach thought it would be a good idea for me to go out for track in the spring to get my speed up. The baseball coach thought it was a good idea too, since it would keep me off the baseball team.

I was never a fast runner, but there were always one or two guys I could beat. As the season drew to a close I took pride in never finishing last.

The final meet of the season for me was the junior varsity state meet. The event was composed of the best mediocre high school runners in Massachusetts. I was in the last heat for the 400 meter, one time around the gravel track. I lined up at the start and glanced to either side trying unsuccessfully to pick out the 300lb lineman or four foot freshman that I could beat.

Then I made a decision. It was time for me to step up to the plate. I had been running track all season and I was going to have to run the race of my life to not lose this one.

The gun sounded, I was out of the gates like a Triple Crown winner. Looking straight ahead, I focused solely on the lane in front of me. As I came into the first turn I knew this was the fastest I had ever run. The other runners and I came into that turn in a dead heat, then they blew by me. At the halfway point it was everyone else, then me.

As I came into the final turn the leaders were approaching the finish and I felt a touch of sadness. I had never cared about winning, but I suddenly realized I did care about losing.

The top two runners battled down the stretch. With a few strides to go one of the runners leaned his chest forward in an effort to best his opponent. With all his might the boy extended towards the finish line, but he stretched a little too far and was propelled face first towards the white line.

As his body slid across the gravel I felt the speed that had propelled me to so many second to last place finishes during the year. I kicked my feet and sprinted down the final straight away past the bleachers and towards the finish.

All the other runners had finished and were getting their times while I ran on. My fallen competitor slowly pushed to his knees, only steps from the finish and began to crawl toward the line. I heard a lone voice call out to me from the stands, "Gooooooo Dinger." As the poor sole crawled towards the line I sprinted past him and threw my arms in the air. I may come in last at some point, but not today. Today I was the second slowest runner, in the last heat, of the junior varsity 400 meter championships.

CHOCOLATE MILK

best through a spiral straw

moosehead

Growing up, taking the bus to school was a pretty daunting experience. All the kids in first through fifth grade rode the same bus to school, and some of the fifth graders were huge. Where you sat on the bus, or who you sat by was a very important decision. By sitting by yourself you were safe for now, but what if some giant came and sat next to you. The only time you were truly safe was when you were sitting by the window and an older girl would come sit next to you providing a buffer to any potential riders. "A cork," I called them.

The most important thing was the bus driver. If the bus driver knew your name he would watch out for you, then you knew you would make it safely to school. Once off the bus there were a myriad of other problems, but getting there safely was a good start.

Ted drove bus number two when I was growing up and always got me to and from school without worry. Ted wore a full beard and half smile that made you feel at ease. He always said "good morning" and "have a good day", and he helped me accomplish that.

I told my parents how much I liked Ted. When he was out we had a guy who played rock and roll too loud, I told my parents I couldn't wait for Ted to come back. At Christmas my parents wanted to give him a present, so they asked around.

At the time it all seemed quite normal, those were simple times. Looking back however, it might have been a little odd to watch a seven year old walk onto the school bus and present the driver with a six-pack of Canadian beer.

fame

The children's eyes opened wide and their mouths even wider as the passed the giant hole dug in the sand on the beach. They stared in amazement for awhile then ran to find their family so they too could witness this crowning achievement of mankind.

The surfers and sun goddesses would stop and check out the hole as they walked along the beach.

"What's it for?" the tourists would ask as they looked down from the rim.

Matty sat stretched out at the bottom of the hole bathing in the mid day sun.

"Matty, were going down the beach to play volleyball, are you in?" I asked.

"No thanks," he answered, a small crowd began to form at ground level high above, "over there I'm just another guy. Here, I'm the guy in the hole."

you never forget

I never had training wheels on my bike, nor did my father run along behind me on the flat street in front of our house. His technique was much simpler, making use of the laws Newton had laid down previously.

Dad brought me to the top of a hill, held me up straight and let me glide down. He chose hills that were rather steep, with a large number of obstacles.

When I accelerated to a speed far greater then any boy who doesn't know how to ride a bike should be traveling I turned off so I wasn't going down at such an extreme angle and crashed into a light pole.

The bike lay before me on the ground. I kicked it for failing to watch where it was going. "It's not the bikes fault," my father explained. I thought about this for a moment and agreed. I gave the light post a solid kick.

When I was in college I got the urge to ride a bike again. I hadn't ridden a bike in years but recalled the saying "It's like riding a bike, you never forget." I borrowed a friend's Cannondale and set off away from town.

As I lay on the ground on the side of the road I made a mental note to be wary of activities which people said were "like riding a bike." Then, remembering the words from my father, I got up and kicked the light post.

minimalist

I worked at an Italian deli in Arizona one summer. When the 120 degree heat got you down you could come in for nice sandwich. A young boy and his mother walked in one Sunday morning. The mother ordered an italian sub with everything, the boy wanted bologna. "Hey pal, do you want mayonnaise," I asked.

"No thank you," he answered.

"Any mustard?"

"No thank you."

"How about some lettuce?"

"Just bologna and bread please?"

I looked at his mother as I layered plain bologna on the roll. "A minimalist," I commented.

She smiled and looked down at her boy. "A dying breed," she said.

shere kahn

Colby stretched his chest up over the counter and looked at the librarian. "Have you seen any snakes in here today," he asked.

"No," answered the librarian, "but the iguana is in the aquarium over by the window."

"Okay," answered Colby and walked away. The librarian thought for a moment and then went back to her filing. A few minutes later Colby returned to the counter and again got on his toes to try and look the librarian in the eye. "Do you have any books on how to catch snakes?"

lemonade stand

In the summer when you are eight years old and need money you set up a lemonade stand. Mary had a distinct advantage over the other kids her age because her family was in the beverage distribution business. This not only cut out the labor of making the drinks, but also with the product free for the taking in the family garage, the profit margin was huge.

One hot sunny day she put out her sign and her beach chair and waited for the quarters to start rolling in. Just when the small company started to turn a profit her grandfather drove up. He walked over to the small table. "Hi sweetie," he said, "how's business?"

"Pretty good," said Mary, "I made three dollars and 25 cents already."

"I tell you what," said Grandpa, "here's ten dollars, I'll take all you have left."

With Mary happily filling dixie cups, her grandfather gazed at the garage. "Suppose I should find a new place to store the beer," he thought to himself.

dogwood

When I was born my father planted a tree in the front yard.

When I was ten I climbed into its branches and watched the clouds drift by.

When I was fifteen I hid behind the tree and threw snowballs at cars coming down the road.

When I was twenty I sat in the shade of the tree and drank warm cans of beer.

When I was twenty-five I pressed my girlfriend up against it's trunk as I kissed her in the dark.

Yesterday I went for a walk past my tree. One of the neighbor's kids was perched in the branches staring down at me. I said hello and asked him how he liked the tree. The boy said it was his favorite. I told him that it was my favorite too, and continued on my walk.

"By the way," I said to the boy pointing at some branches, "If you rest your head in that 'V' you can lay back perfectly and look up at the clouds, never throw snowballs at vans, and there's a case of Budweiser behind the bikes in our garage."

The boy looked down at me as if he were waiting for me to say something else. I looked back at the boy in my tree and shrugged, "other things are still pretty confusing, but I'll let you know if I figure anything out."

ice cream

Being a kid having your father take you to Fenway Park for a Red Sox game is about as good as it gets. You get to see the players from television up close, get an autograph, and have a boiled hot dog, all in one beautiful park.

As you grow up and the world starts to become more and more complicated, it's nice to have Fenway to go back to. It helps simplify things. A lot of people say baseball is too slow, but that's precisely what I love about baseball. Things move pretty fast in the real world. In the baseball park there's no clock on the wall counting down the seconds until the game ends; the relief pitcher takes his time as he walks in from the bullpen; and when someone hits a home run it's worth the same amount no matter how long it takes to run along the bases.

I sat with my friend Steffen at a game in April. Sitting in front of us were a father with his young son and daughter. Watching the boy stare in awe at the field and the sea of people around it took me back. Sitting in that red seat the boy hadn't a care in the world, no idea when the electric bill was due, no worries as to why the car was making that humming noise, and no comprehension of compound interest.

After the sixth inning the kid's father got up to go to the rest room and big Sis was left in charge. An ice cream vendor passed up the aisle going the other way. "Sport's Baaaaars," he yelled. A large button was pinned to his chest reading "$3.50."

"I remember when they were a dollar," Steffen said to the vender.

The vendor looked at him and smiled, "And I remember you," he said. "Sport's Baaaaars."

The young boy's mouth opened to a wide smile. He raised his hand towards the vendor. "Here," he said happily. Just when you think things can't get any better a man comes around with ice cream bars. The vendor turned to the boy and looked at his big sister. She shook her head no and the vendor continued down the aisle.

"No, you have to buy them," the little girl explained. The boy's jaw dropped farther down and the wide smile turned into an open mouth. The shine blurred in his eyes and it all began to come together. Ice cream isn't free, somebody has to pay the rent, somebody has to pay to fix the car, and every day the electric bill goes without being paid the interest is compounding.

"Hey Ice cream," Steffen shouted and pointed at the boy. Maybe that will buy the boy another week, or another day without care I thought. However long it lasts, those are precious times, well worth $3.50.

replay

Game six of the 1975 World Series is considered by many the greatest game ever played. The contest went back and forth between the Red Sox and the Reds for twelve inning before Carlton Fisk waved a home run fair to win the game.

I wasn't alive when the game was originally played, however it was occasionally replayed on television. Red Sox fans haven't had too many World Series moments to cheer about so my father would always watch it.

When I was five I watched it with him for the first time. Mom went to bed when Bernie Carbo hit the pinch hit home run to tie the game. When the Red Sox squandered an opportunity in the bottom of the ninth it was well past the hour when I was normally put asleep.

Both teams showed signs of fatigue as the game entered the twelfth inning and I began to feel the effects of staying up past my bed time. "If Carlton Fisk doesn't hit a home run this inning I'm going to bed," my father said.

"Me too," I agreed. At eleven o'clock on that winter night I danced around the living room in celebration of the Red Sox win. Although the game was played before I was born, that night I sat with my father and got to watch it live.

MOJITO

refreshing for travels near & far

COWS

In Vimy Ridge, France there is a memorial for Canadian soldiers who lost there lives in the First World War. The marble monument is located next to an old battlefield. Craters pock the ground from all the exploded shells and a a fence separates the battlefield from the grounds of the memorial.

The guide explained to Chris and I that there may still be live explosives left over on the grounds. "Unfortunately," he continued, "over the years a few cows have wandered into the field and discovered this."

Chris smiled, "Where's the memorial for the cows."

imagine

I sat back in the grass on the cliff and looked out towards the ocean far below. Behind me I could just see water on the other side of the peninsula peeking out from behind the green hills. A slow breeze weaved its way through the far trees cooling me before disappearing into the forest beside me.

This, I thought, is what I will think of when I am back in the world and told to imagine being in a beautiful place.

more or less

When you head off the beaten path the walkways aren't often paved. The people in Central America would do their best to let you know how to get to these spots without getting hurt. There were a few things I learned in my travels that helped me to better understand what they really meant.

A fellow traveler and I were talking to a friend we had met in Montezuma, Costa Rica. He was explaining to us how to reach a waterfall that emptied into the ocean. He told us how spectacular it was to see, and how one would swim underneath the falls and gaze up at the water coming down. Almost in passing he cautioned, make sure you come back before high tide or razor sharp rocks will rip you apart.

"Well, is it safe", we asked, "Would you like to come?" He assured us that it was very safe, but he couldn't make it. "No, but you go," he answered. I learned to be wary of "No, but you go."

"We're going for a late night swim, do you want to come?" I asked another friend. "No, but you go. Just make sure you don't go in over your head... and don't kick your legs around too much, many sharks at night."

"Es posible" is another phrase that I heard a lot. "Can you hike to that beach down there?" I asked. "Es posible." This means "I heard of someone doing it one time, but usually stupid tourists just fall down and break their legs. "Es posible" often goes hand in hand with "no, but you go," but is a little more dangerous.

My favorite saying dealt more with distance then danger. "La cascada es 3 kilómetros lejos, más o menos," literally translates to "the waterfall is 3 kilometers away, more or less." However, after going on a few all day hikes I found "más o menos" lost a little in the translation. What it really means is "I have no freakin' idea how far away the waterfall is, but it sure as hell is farther then 3 kilometers."

translation

The menus in Costa Rica were often written with English on one side and Spanish on the other. They served many wonderful fresh fruit drinks there, which are served with either water or milk. While deciding on a juice drink one day I noticed my menu read "with water 100 colones with milk 150 colones - con agua 100 colones con leche 125 colones." I decided to order my drink "con leche" and save the 25 colones.

At the Hotel Nacional in Havana there are two 100 year old cannons outside the gardens pointed toward the great harbor. Next to the cannon are two iron plaques written side by side in Spanish and English. The plaque tells the history of the cannons in the 1898 War of Independence and how they once fired upon the American armada while they tried to enter Havana Harbor. The only difference in the verbiage is that the English side has one extra line. It reads "none of the ships were hit."

driving

I once acquired a first class seat to Boston from Phoenix. Being a common man, this was quite a treat, and one which I decided to take full advantage of.

We first stopped in Las Vegas where I learned you can drink on the ground in any airport in the country except in the city of sin. I'm not sure why this is so, but I'm guessing there is a good reason. Somewhere out there is the guy responsible for alcohol being banned on the ground at Las Vegas airport. He is probably having a drink with the man with a metal plate in his head who got lawn darts taken off the market.

After finishing my filet with another airplane bottle of vodka, the captain came on the loudspeaker and said we were nearing Boston. I decided to have one last vodka before we touched down.

"Sir will you be driving later," the stewardess asked as she poured the drink over ice. "If you would like" I said, "but isn't that what the guy up front in the hat is for?"

water taxi

Bocas Del Torro is a group of islands located just off the eastern coast of Panama. Bocas is as beautiful as it is undeveloped, and the days of the week drift past without a care of whether or not they begin with the letter "S".

I spent most of my time on the island of Bassimento, staying in the one group of cabinas on the island. My room was attached to a small bar/restaurant out on stilts in the water. My front door opened to the vast Caribbean Sea and through the back door I could watch the waves wash up on the island's shore. There was a long dock that stretched from shore to the wooden structure and out into the Ocean. Water Taxi's would occasionally shuttle people to and from the dock of "el pelicano".

The day before my departure I arranged for a boy to pick me up and shuttle me to the main island where I would catch the boat to the mainland. In retrospect I now realize the boy I hired had no idea what I was saying in my broken Spanish and would have agreed to swim with me on his back if I had asked. The hour of his arrival came and went and I came to the conclusion I needed to find other transportation.

I knew there was one other bar not far away, so I strapped on my pack, bid farewell to my friends and set out to find it. Once at the bar I asked the bartender if there was anyone around who could shuttle me to the big island. A few American dollars are a lot of money to islanders and a table of teenagers jumped up, ecstatic to take me. Unfortunately, the older Captain was too drunk to take on the mission himself and also in no hurry to leave the bar.

Each boy argued his case as to why he should be the one to drive the boat, and eventually one was chosen. I piled in the boat with the boys where after some last minute instructions from the Captain, we were on our way.

Not long into the journey I realized the error of my decision. Although, more sober then the Captain, the boys were all "muy baracho." Flying around the ocean in a dug out canoe with an outboard motor driven by a drunken teenage pilot with whom I could barely communicate made me a little nervous. The most sober of the boys asked if I could swim. I lied and said I could not, and he assured me he would relay the information to the driver and we would take a slower and more direct route to the island. If it were not for my backpack I am sure I would have bailed overboard and swam for the island.

A good rule of thumb I now use is: When looking for a water taxi, bars are probably not the best spots to find one, especially late in the afternoon

vice president

My father imported printing ink from Japan. He found the Japanese to be excellent business men, but very formal. During this time he traveled to Japan on a number of occasions.

On one of these trips his hosts took him to a shop that sold signs written in kanji, the Japanese characters. Today, college freshman invariably tattoo a Japanese sign for wisdom, love, or whatever their girlfriend of the moment thinks is appropriate. At the time my father had not seen the characters and was taken with the intricacy and beauty of the forms. He browsed through the shop and asked the meaning of different signs.

He found one sign in particular to be most beautiful. The symbols, although separate, sat on the wooden background as if they were only meant to be together. "I would like this sign," my father told the man who was escorting him around the city. "Oh, Mr. Richard, you do not want that sign," the man informed him. The Japanese man then explained the meaning, but my father insisted and brought the sign back to the U.S.

Later, he and his associates from Japan returned to the U.S. My father took them into the office of his vice president and took out the sign. "Ben," he said to his colleague," it is apparent to all of us that this company could not function without you. I wanted to say thank you, so when I traveled to Japan I got you this gift. My father then presented him with the sign. Ben was as taken with the sign as my father and held it out to look at.

"Richard, this is gorgeous, what does it say?"

"It says, Vice president."

"That's great, I'm going to put this up in my office, or maybe I'll put it in my car," Ben said. In the end he decided to display it in the back window of his car where everyone he passed could enjoy it as well.

My father and the Japanese men left the room and walked towards the warehouse. The other men had stayed as stone faced as a judge while in the meeting but as they left they couldn't contain themselves any longer. "Mr. Richard, you give him the sign that say bathroom."

marketing genius

On the up side I found the bus station I was looking for very easily, on the down side I found out there are many bus stations in San Jose, Costa Rica and buses don't go to Santa Elena from the Coca-Cola bus station.

When I finally arrived at the right station and purchased my ticket I was relieved to have reserved seat number fifty-four. It was a five hour ride to Santa Elena. On the walk to the station I decided that if all they had was standing room I would spend the night in the city and leave first thing tomorrow.

Ten minutes later the bus arrived and everyone began to cram on. I moved towards the back of the bus and read the numbers above the seats, 38-39-40. I was exhausted from my extensive unscheduled tour of downtown San Jose, 48-49-50.

When I reached the last row of seats I reexamined my ticket. The aisle behind me was crammed full of backpackers, Costa Rican travelers, and children.

"What seat number do you have?" I asked a backpacker standing near me in the aisle.

"Sixty-Five," he answered as the bus learched forward.

home field advantage

My brother and I stood at mile 20 of the Boston marathon as the leaders ran by.

"Looks like it is going to be another Kenyan winning this year," I said, " Did you know Kenyans have won the marathon the last ten years."

My brother nodded, "Everyone knows that," he answered, "but did you know that every year a Bostonian wins the Kenyan marathon?"

hitchhiker

Luke had an idea for an advertising campaign and decided he wanted to drive to California to present it to the head of marketing at Nike. For his journey from Boston he was given his parents station wagon.

Before making the trip he made a few aesthetic alterations to the car. Luke and his friends spray painted farewell wishes, a '23' on the front for his favorite basketball player, an American flag was attached to the antenna, and a pair of Texas long horns were mounted on the front. If it wasn't for the wood paneling on the side Mom and Dad wouldn't have even been able to recognize the 1973 Country Squire.

Luke set off on his mission with a thousand dollars and an interesting cross of naiveté and youthful bravery. He spent two months on his cross country voyage, sleeping on a mattress in the back of the station wagon and bathing in the pools of unknowing hotels.

Driving along a lonely road in Kentucky late one night he saw a bearded man with his thumb out by the side of the road. There were no other cars in site and Luke needed gas money, so he stopped to pick the man up.

The two drove along through the darkness. The man had been moving around for years hitchhiking from one side of the country to the other and back again. He got by any way he could and often found himself in situations where he thought he may not see the light of day. Luke told the man how he had just graduated college and was making his way home from California.

The man looked at the youthful smile of the boy, "There are a lot of crazies out there," he told him, "you shouldn't pick up people like me."

Luke stared through the windshield past the tattered flag, over the giant red and white '23' spray painted on the hood, past the bull horns and eyed the dark road ahead. "What did you think when I stopped to pick you up?" he asked.

The man ran his fingers over the hair on his face, gray from his years on the road, "I was scared to get in."

mail buoy

Aaron got a job on a boat mapping the ocean floor. They traversed back and fourth looking out over miles of open water.

"Hey Cap, what's that stuff about the mail buoy on the board," Aaron asked.

"Funny you ask," the captain began, "ours is a profession rich in history. In the past ships would often be at sea for months, if not years at a time without two-way radios, cell phone's, email or any reliable means to communicate with loved ones. The government dropped these mail buoys at remote spots around the ocean and sailors could leave letters that would then be picked up and delivered. Mostly out of tradition they keep a few of these active, but with helicopters having to come in and pick up the mail I'm not sure how much longer it will last."

"Aaron, do you have any stamps?" someone yelled across the boat.

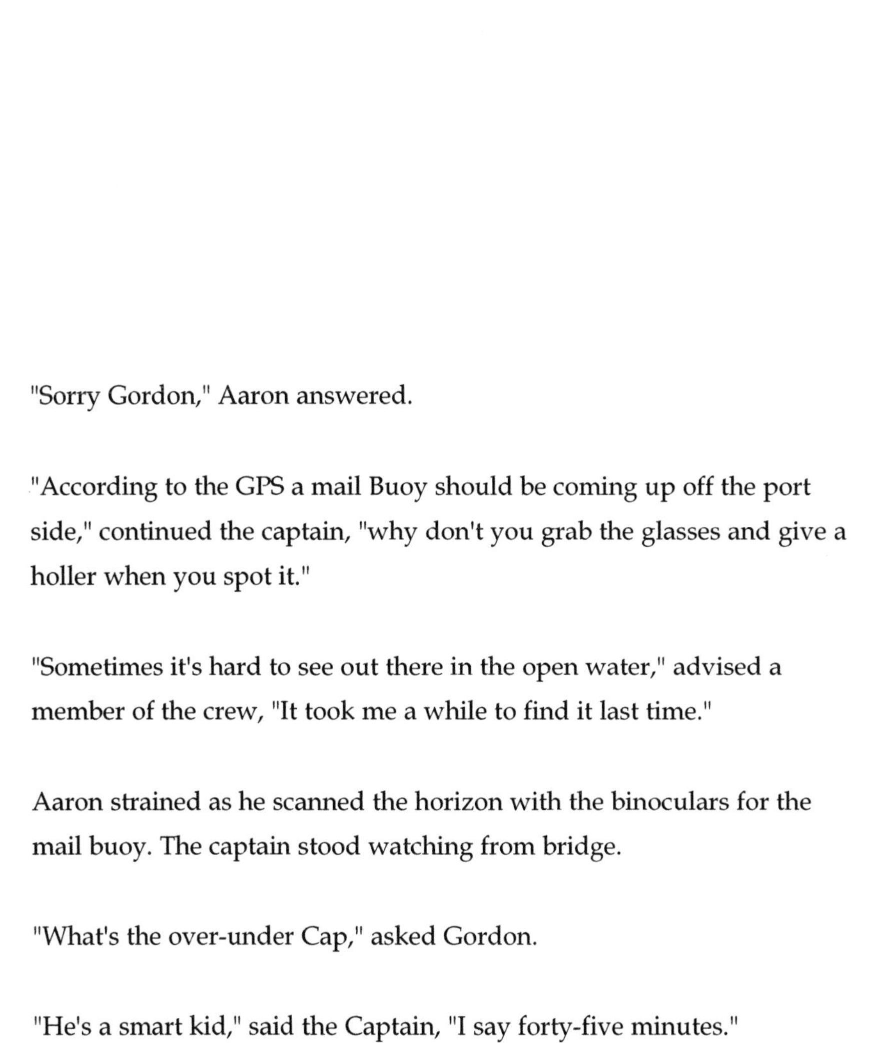

"Sorry Gordon," Aaron answered.

"According to the GPS a mail Buoy should be coming up off the port side," continued the captain, "why don't you grab the glasses and give a holler when you spot it."

"Sometimes it's hard to see out there in the open water," advised a member of the crew, "It took me a while to find it last time."

Aaron strained as he scanned the horizon with the binoculars for the mail buoy. The captain stood watching from bridge.

"What's the over-under Cap," asked Gordon.

"He's a smart kid," said the Captain, "I say forty-five minutes."

i wish i didn't know

Tavio and I sat on a peak above the valleys of Pinar Del Rio, Cuba. Fields of tan and green stretched out forever guarded by pincushion mountains. I followed the path of a car driving down a lone dirt road through the valley, and then laughed out loud.

"When we would approach the city of Boston," I explained to Tavio, "my friend would ask the guy in the tollbooth which exit he should take for Yankee Stadium. The guy would always get very flustered and tell us that we were in Boston and the Yankees played in New York 100 miles away." I laughed again as I thought about the faces of the toll collectors as they took our money.

The sound of my laughter was taken towards the hills as a soft breeze cooled the hot air, Tavio looked out over the open land and then stared back blankly, "What's a tollbooth?"

there is time

I felt a little on edge when I first went to Cuba. The people would come up to me and tell me stories of their country, ask questions about America, advise me as to all the wonderful places I should visit, then they would smile and go about their day. I kept waiting for the hook at the end when they would ask if I wanted to buy a necklace, or for them to give me a tour.

Eventually, I realized that the Cuban people just genuinely wanted to talk, and to smile, and to learn, and to laugh. There isn't really any poverty, because everyone is poor. Communism doesn't lead to prosperity, but it does breed a very relaxed way of life. The people know they aren't going to be millionaires, but they know they will eat and have a roof over their heads; there isn't a lot to worry about.

I took a cab ride in a beautiful '57 ford to visit Hemingway's house outside of Havana. Ignacio drove me. He told me of his life in Cuba, and his love for his country. Ignacio swelled when he talked of his children and smiled when he talked of his wife. We slowly trotted through small towns on the way to the Museo Hemingway. Children played baseball in the street, women sat on their porches watching the world go by, Ignacio and I drove by in second gear.

I shook my head when Ignacio asked me if I was married. He smiled as he sat back in his seat and slowly rolled down the dirt road, "Hay tiempo," he said.

BEAJULAIS

light & fruity

pb&j

Big Josh worked for a year taking care of the grounds at a mansion overlooking the ocean. "They had a huge wine cellar," he told me, "for lunch we would have peanut butter and jelly and a bottle of wine that cost more then a day's pay."

"Which wine goes best with peanut butter and jelly?" I asked. Josh thought about the question and reminisced about his year as a landscaper. "A young Beaujolais is nice in the summertime, when it gets cooler I like fluffernutter and twenty year old Douro Valley Port."

erosion

My first tour of duty in college was spent at Arizona State University. If I were a guidance counselor I would recommend every senior that they spend some time there. No adolescent male from the East Coast will ever be able to travel to this oasis of bikini clad coeds and nickel drafts and graduate, but there is no nicer school in the country to fail out of.

Some classmates and I took a trip north to the Grand Canyon one weekend, or quite possibly it was mid-week; who wanted to miss a weekend at school. Many writers more talented than I have failed in trying to transfer the canyon's vast beauty to words on a page so I will spare you the effort, except to say that it is greater in reality then one can imagine.

As we hiked deeper down into the canyon and the sun dropped deeper down into the sky we took a few shortcuts through the brush to expediate our trip towards the bottom. At one point a park ranger stopped us and said to stick to the trail or we would cause the canyon to erode. "Ma'am," my friend Glenn explained "if it wasn't for erosion none of us would be here in the first place."

rowing

John loves the Miami Dolphins. Unfortunately their annual December collapse has tormented him for many years. One season after watching his beloved team get eliminated from contention as the weather turned cold he went a little overboard and impaled the TV with a nearby lamp. Moments later his parents returned home and decided that it might be best for John to talk with a psychiatrist.

John didn't have a lot of leverage at this point and agreed to go once a week for the next two months. John answered all the doctors' questions as candidly as he would to anyone. They looked at ink blots and talked about his week.

As the clock neared one o'clock in his last session John asked a question of his own, "So Doc, am I crazy?" John waited for the Doctor to explain that he was perfectly normal, just a bit high strung when it comes to sports. "Well John," the psychiatrist finally answered sitting back in his chair and clasping his palms together, "I wouldn't say you're crazy, but you definitely don't have both oars in the water."

working from home

Mark stopped by his boss' office on the way out the door Thursday. "The cable guy's coming sometime between ten and four tomorrow so I'm going to be working from home."

"Mark you always get your projects done on time, and that's all I really care about," his boss replied, "but, do you have to make quotation marks in the air when you say working?"

absolute

I made my share of mistakes while growing up. At the time they were complete injustices on the part of the authority. "I was thrown out of class for no reason again, Mr. Harris," I recall explaining to the principal.

As I got a little older I began to learn that my actions were my own responsibility, and that there was a reason I was asked to leave class all those days in school. Then alcohol entered the fray and I found that as much as I had changed, much had stayed the same. "I was thrown out of the bar for no reason again," I recall explaining to my girlfriend.

I was lucky enough to grow up with my grandfather living on the other side of the block. He was a great man, and a great listener. Bumpa would always tell me what he thought, but never what to do.

One day I cut through the neighbors' yard and walked up the hill to visit him. Bumpa was never a big drinker, but he liked to have a beer when he watched the Red Sox game. Anyone who roots for the same team for seventy years and never sees them win a world series needs something to soften the heart break. He offered me one and I told him I didn't really like the taste of beer, and when I went out, I drank hard alcohol.

"There's nothing wrong with that," he said, "as long as you don't drink vodka." Bumpa sat in his leather chair in front of the TV and watched the Red Sox batter step into the box as he had so many times before.

"When you drink anything else people can smell it on you and they know you're drunk," he continued, "the problem with vodka is you can't smell it, so people just think you're stupid."

halfway hal's pizza

Halfway Hal is known for starting projects, getting halfway done, and then moving on to something more interesting.

Hal's phone number is the same as a popular pizza place in Southie except his last digit is two and the pizza place's is three. When hungry Bostonian's aren't able to reach all the way across the keypad to the three and inadvertently hit the two they are rewarded with Halfway Hal.

Hal probably gets 3 phone calls a night from people looking for pizza. At first he was nice and explained to them that it was a wrong number but after a while that got boring. I asked him what he has said to these people, "anything you can imagine we have done", he explained.

On cue the phone rang. "Hello", Hal answered, "... I don't really feel like making pizza tonight, why don't you get some Chinese food."

meetings

Uncle Donald worked for the same company from the time he graduated from college, until he retired. Donald liked his work, and liked getting things done, what he didn't like was bureaucracy.

In corporate America there are a lot of people who love meetings, meetings about direction, meetings about systems, meetings about having more meetings. Everyone is required to be there even if only remotely involved. People sometimes think that the more people they invite to their meeting the more important they are. Once in the meeting there are those people who have to bring you through every possible "what if", dragging things on through pointless scenarios.

Donald hated meetings. Unfortunately, there are times when they cannot be avoided. After his many years with the company he found that he could keep his meetings short, and to the point by having the room arranged properly. Whenever he had to call a meeting Donald would call up building services and have the room set up to his liking.

Donald would walk in and thank everyone for coming, and then almost always the first question was the same. A new employee would look around and ask, "Where are all the chairs?"

spiral staircase

Mr. Walker was my favorite teacher. Some teachers say that there are no stupid questions, to Mr. Walker there were plenty. When students would ask how long a paper should be, he would always reply, "Twice as long," and move on. Mr. Walker taught for 40 years at the same high school, "you will come and you will go," he would say, "I will be here forever."

Every day we had vocabulary words that would have to be defined for homework, and every Friday we would have a quiz, "regular as rain," he would say. I learned that if I had forgotten to do the homework and was called on to define a word in class I would answer with something random like "a spiral staircase." A spiral staircase could be a good second meaning for any word and on occasion the teacher would think that you had just picked an obscure definition.

One Friday Tom and I were studying for the quiz in the moments before class and we came to the word "loquacious". I always remembered the word because when girls wouldn't talk to me I would ask why they weren't very loquacious, and sometimes they would think I was smart. That was pretty much my best line back then, so until alcohol got put into the equation, not a lot of girls talked to me. Tom, however, could not remember the definition.

Kids would always complain about the number of words we had to study, "You only have to study ten," Mr. Walker would tell them, "The trick is knowing which ten I am going to ask you." Tom had unfortunately studied the wrong ten and "loquacious" was one of the words on the quiz.

After Mr. Walker read all ten words we would switch papers with the person to our left and as our teacher went over the definitions we would correct the papers. When we got to "loquacious" the girl who was correcting Tom's paper raised her hand. "Tom wrote 'whatever Dave has,'" she said confused at how to mark the paper. Mr. Walker paused and then asked if Dave had gotten the question right. Once informed that I had, he remarked, "Well then Tom is correct."

ed bruce

I went with my brother to the car dealership. We walked around the lot and stopped at a nice SUV. Will sat in the leather seat and examined the controls on the dash.

A salesman walked over and extended his hand. "This is a good looking truck," my brother said to him.

"We just got her in yesterday." the salesman said. "My names Ed Bruce, great to meet you."

"Well thanks for letting me look at her, I have to get going," my brother said abruptly. Ed Bruce tried to get Will to take the truck for a test drive, but he was ready to go.

"What's wrong," I asked as we drove away. My brother looked back at me and held his finger out as he spoke, "Never trust a man with two first names."

psychic

Steph burst into the living room. "I went to the psychic today and I learned so much. I know people don't believe in them but she was amazing. She told me things about myself that there's no way she could know, things that nobody knows.

"What did she tell you?" I asked.

"Well," Steph began and then stopped to organize all the things the psychic had talked about in their hour together, "she said I was confused."

wedding

Paul dated Sarah for five years and she became quite close with his family. After they broke up he tried to keep a cordial relationship, but after seeing her reaction to him on a few chance meetings he knew that this would be impossible.

None the less, at his mother's request Paul invited her to attend his father's 50th birthday party. Sarah sent back a note gushing about how happy she was now and that she was getting married that summer. "Sorry I can't make your fathers 50th birthday, I'm going to an appetizer tasting that night for my wedding" Sarah wrote, "but I'll be sure and make the next one."

Paul wrote back, "Sorry you can't make the party. Unfortunately, I will be out of the country this summer and unable to attend your wedding, but I'll be sure to make the next one."

higher education

One fall day early in the school year I found myself in the cafeteria searching for inspiration for my stomach. One of the other students was standing in dismay by the beverage station.

There were a couple of clear plexiglas drink machines in the cafeteria that would mix up iced tea, fruit punch, or in this case HI-C. To the dismay of this other student previous lovers of that wonderful elixir had emptied the HI-C machine.

"Hey, this drink machine is empty," he notified the women running the cash register. "I'll get to it," she replied in a tone that said have a coke and come back tomorrow. He looked at the coke in the cooler and back at the cashier, "I pay twenty G's to go here; I want the HI-C filled now."

life

The summer after Fritz's senior year in high school he dated Annie. Annie was a beautiful girl, and as with most beautiful seventeen year olds Annie's father was an intimidating man, which was exponentially true if you were dating his daughter.

When Fritz came by to pick her up Annie's father answered the door. Fritz was informed that Annie would be down in a minute and was invited to sit down. Every muscle in Fritz's body was tensed as he relaxed on the couch. "What are you going to do Fritz," Annie's father asked.

Fritz was hoping to get out of they're with just talk of baseball and the weather but apparently this would be impossible. For the last two years everyone had been pressuring him into going to this college or that college, telling him what he should do with his life.

Fortunately, by this time he had developed a polished answer and was ready to justify his future existence in the hopes of getting out the door with young Annie. "In the Fall I will be attending college upstate and majoring in communications with a minor in film. A lot of students major in film at the school, but I believe that a broader major like communications will give me more leeway in case I decide that I want to do something different down the road. My uncle has a production company in Boston and has already offered me an internship next summer, which will help me to get some real world experience on my resume. I think that having that job experience and hopefully by then a few references is what is going to help me land a good job in four years."

Annie's father sat quietly in his leather chair with his feet up on the ottoman; he stroked his beard with his right hand and rhythmically tapped his fingers with his left. Fritz had loosened up when he got going on his answer but again sat tensely as the silence built between them. Annie's father removed his hand from his beard and leaned forward. "Fritz, what are you going to do tonight?"

lent

Laura was an amazing woman. She raised six kids that have done more to help the less fortunate than some small states. All the while, she smiled and laughed, and was a joy to everyone who was lucky enough to meet her.

When she passed away, her husband shared a story which always brings her sense of humor back to me. A friend of one of the kids came over during lent and told her proudly that he had given up swearing for lent. "Good for fuckin' you," Laura told him.

CABERNET SOUVIGNON

deep, full bodied

dewey points

Darren went up to heaven and walked towards the gates, where he was met by a young boy. "Hello Darren," said the boy, "I'm here to judge your life."

"Please excuse me, I've had a rough morning," said Darren, "but aren't you a little young to be determining how people spend eternity?"

"It's okay, people always ask that," said the boy. "When people grow up everyone tells them what they're supposed to do and they start to forget what really matters. Kids are left alone to play and haven't already forgotten what everybody once knew."

"So what does really matter?" asked Darren.

"That's funny," said the boy, "nobody's ever asked me that before." He laughed out loud, amused at the joke he had told so many times before. "When you walk down to the bus stop it is measured in miles, when you go to the nurse she weighs you in pounds, when you buy a comic book the man charges you in dollars. People measure a lot of stuff. We measure in Dewey points. A Dewey point is like one pound of happiness. When you see a shooting star and for one moment you get that happy feeling inside, that's one Dewey point, when you make your little sister smile when she's sick that's like ten Dewey points, and when Julie kisses you on the cheek that's like fifty hundred Dewey points.

"Who's Julie?" asked Darren.

"Darren, try and keep up, it doesn't matter who Julie is," answered the boy. "When you come here we add up all your points and all the points you have helped others get and that's how we judge your life. Even a kid could do it." Again the boy laughed heartily at his joke and then looked back at Darren.

"That's it," said Darren.

"Simple, huh," said the boy.

dreams

I woke up with butterflies in my stomach, a long hair on my shirt. I had a feeling inside that wouldn't go away. A feeling you get when you're with a girl that gives you a feeling inside. I new it was leftover from last night, but not who it was from?

I love the moments in the morning when you first wake up, before it all comes back. Sometimes the feelings come first, sometimes the smell of perfume, or better no perfume at all, the way someone talks, a look from across the room. A snapshot somehow burned into your memory deeper then any other moment allowing you to glimpse, but not enough to remember.

I held the hair between my fingers and watched the morning light shine red and amber off its long, smooth curves. I began to see her smile, hear her laugh; seeing her again for the first time.

I sat on the edge of my bed and stared at the door knob. The nice thing about sleeping in your clothes is you don't have to get dressed in the morning.

Jon was making coffee in the kitchen. He had the want ads spread out on the table. Jon loved to read about all the strange things that people wanted to sell.

"Did you see me talking to anyone at the end of the night?" I asked. "I remember talking to this beautiful girl, with a big smile, and she laughed at my jokes. But I can't decide if I dreamt about her, or she was real."

Jon looked up from the paper, his eyebrows were slightly lowered and his mouth was tightened in thought. He stared through me for quite a while. Before he returned to his morning perusal of the weeks classifieds for water damaged Playboys and pygmy goats he slowly spoke. "If dreams and memories sometimes get confused, then maybe that's the way it's supposed to be."

tick

You sit back and look at your life. You crunch all the numbers and run through all the possible scenarios of where you can go from here. Eventually you come up with the answer to what you should do. What the intelligent thing to do is; the calculated, premeditated, well planned out path that will lead you to where you want to go.

The left side of your brain takes all that evidence and argues the well devised merits of the plan to the right side. Clearly this plan will lead to common goals of both sides of the brain.

The right side of your brain just says, "Screw it, your plan sucks, I'm getting on a plane today. Life is short and the clock is ticking."

So you think about it and walk through the path of getting on that plane today. You contemplate every variable in that plan, and no matter how many different ways you look at it things never end up as well as the left brain's plan. It's just like when you ran the numbers the first time.

As you walk away and glance down at your watch you know the right side is right about one thing.

news

"Where's all the newspapers," Todd asked his manager.

"The airport's fogged in, so they haven't been able to deliver them yet," he answered. "That's what we get living on an island."

A customer walked in and after a quick glance around walked up to Todd and asked for the Times. "I'm sorry," said Todd, "not this morning."

The man was on Island for the week and had been coming to the store each morning for his paper. He looked up at the manager for a second opinion who in turn shook his head and walked towards the back of the store. "How can there be no paper?" he asked, annoyed at the situation.

Todd gazed out the front window at the lazy Nantucket morning. In the fall the crowds that accompany the summer weather have since gone home. A lone man sat on a row of benches on Main Street sipping his coffee, a taxi was parked along the usually packed strip waiting for someone to drive, two birds fought over the crumbs from a muffin.

The man impatiently tapped his foot as Todd returned his gaze and spoke, "Nothing happened."

lucky

My grandfather always said he was the luckiest man he knew. He lived for 87 years in the same house, high on a hill where he could watch the world change around him. He was married for over 50 years to the same women who had grown up in the town next door. He graduated from law school, yet decided he would rather be a carpenter. He did what made him happy, and didn't worry too much about the details.

A set of train tracks ran through the town where he and I grew up. As years passed, the trains came less frequently until the line was shut down. One last train was scheduled to run through Weston to see if there was anything along the side of the tracks that needed to be picked up before underbrush would maintain the area once more.

My grandfather was putting a roof on a house near the outskirts of town that day. The sun was directly over head and the black shingles sucked up the heat. Bumpa decided it was time for lunch. He got in his red pickup truck and headed toward town. Major intersections with the train tracks had barriers which came down as a train approached, but here you had to check for yourself for oncoming locomotives. Telling this story I am often reminded of the SAT's, when a train leaves Weston going 98 MPH and a truck leaves here going 23 MPH...

"I thought I could make it," my grandfather told me years later. "When I saw it coming I had to either hit the break or the gas, I chose the gas." Bumpa hit the gas and sped over the tracks, all except the bed of his pickup. The train drove right through the back of his truck spinning him out of control until he finally came to a stop in the brush beside the tracks. The red pickup truck wasn't going to make it one more year as he had hoped.

Bumpa set out on foot down the road until he found a phone to call my father. "Dick," he said, "I got hit by a train, can you come pick me up?"

health

I walked inside and Dano jumped off the couch "This is the greatest day of my life," he exclaimed. Dano poured the end of a bottle of red wine into a pint glass and handed it to me. "Did you hear the news, it's finally official."

I thought back about what he might be so excited about. In his excitement Dano didn't give me too long to ponder. "The doctors announced it today; red wine is good for you. They have been talking about it for years, but it's finally official. For once we caught a break."

Steffen got up, raised his glass, and we toasted our good fortune. As we sat back down Steffen smiled and looked out the window. He took a long drink and licked his lips, "I can't wait for the announcement that bacon is good for you."

guitar

My grandfather was always good at talking to people. He listened to what people had to say and always managed to ask just the right questions.

One family he did a lot of work for had a boy who was a great guitar player and, true to the part, a little off center. Bumpa was called to come in and replace a window the boy had broken in retaliation for being punished by his parents.

The boy, confined to his room, was sitting on his bed when my grandfather came in.

"What happened to the window?" he asked looking at the teenager.

"I smashed it," the boy answered bluntly.

"How did you manage that," Bumpa enquired.

"I smashed it with my guitar," he answered.

My grandfather measured the window, then looked at the guitar sitting on its stand in the front of the room. "Why didn't you use a chair or something," Bumpa asked, "I wouldn't want to hurt the guitar."

cliché

Fritz sometimes wonders aloud about the magical place where people leave pies cooling on the windowsill. On TV you see it all the time.

If I ever am lucky enough to come across a hot apple pie left to cool on some windowsill in Utopia I think I will have to steal it. Some things are just too cliché to pass up.

balmy

It can only be balmy in the fall. It's too warm in the spring and summer. There is nothing balmy at all about the winter. In the fall there are those rare sunny days whose temperatures have no business hanging around in October or November, yet there they are.

I was walking through Allston one balmy fall morning. The sun warmed my skin and the cool air was almost tangible as it passed through my nose, down the back of my throat, and into my lungs. The trees in the park were painted orange and gold on a sky blue canvas. "Fall in New England," I thought, "is winter in the mountains, summer at the beach, spring on a baseball diamond."

I passed two bums leaning up against the entrance to an ATM. "This is a beautiful time of year," one of them said to the other.

sunday

There's nothing better then waking up to the sound of the rain falling against your window on a Sunday morning. It's been a long week, the Sunday paper is waiting, and there's no pressure from a beautiful day to go outside and enjoy it.

Rain on a Sunday is somebody saying, I understand, take today off and regroup.

the beholder

It is said that beauty is in the eye of the beholder. More often beauty is seen through the eyes of one who wishes to behold. Once the beauty is held in your arms you sometimes forget what it is that you are holding. What a short time ago it was that you watched from across the room, wishing of one day being able to watch her as she slept. Being able to stare without fear at her face, listening to the sounds of her breath slowly passing in and out of her body, not having to share perfection with every man who was lucky enough to have walked in the room.

Too often once beheld, the beauty loses the glow that kept you up so many nights in the summer. The shine is never as bright in your arms as it was when you watched her walk across the room that first time.

However, even the shine from that first glance across the room cannot begin to compete with the beauty she beholds when she walks away.

magic

A girl I was once dating cheated on me with her ex-boyfriend. I had so many emotions floating around inside me; anger, sadness, betrayal. Most of all I just felt so stupid for falling for a girl who would do this to me. I wanted to talk to someone about how I felt, but at the same time talking to other people just made me feel more stupid. She cheated on me.

As I lay on my back on the living room floor my oldest friend walked in and started to lick my face. He wasn't allowed in the living room, but he was an old dog so we gave him some leeway.

Magic was a Bouvier Des Flanders. A 125lb sheepherding dog that looks like he weighs about 200 with his bushy black coat. When he would walk into a tree you knew it was time to trim the fur around his eyes.

Magic laid down next to me on his stomach with his head pointed straight ahead, his eyes looking straight at me behind freshly trimmed bangs.

I let it all out. I told him everything about how I really felt, what I wanted to do, and how it wasn't going to happen. I stopped acting like I thought I was supposed to act, or feeling like I thought a stronger person should feel. I said everything that I had wanted to say since it happened.

When I finished he lifted his head up slightly off the ground and tilted a little toward one side. Magic looked deep into my eyes and gave me that look that dogs sometimes give you. To let you know that they understand, that they understand everything better then you or I could ever comprehend. Then he let out one of the more baritone belches I have heard in all my days and replaced his head on the floor.

After that Magic and I kept our conversations to small talk of weather and current events.

ABOUT THE AUTHOR

G.D. Harding was born in Weston, Massachusetts. In 2000 after numerous attempts he graduated from college with a degree in graphic design. *advice from my dog* is his first book. Currently he lives year round on Nantucket.